READY TO **READ** COLLECTION

This book belongs to

First Published 2010 by Brown Watson
The Old Mill, 76 Fleckney Road,
Kibworth Beauchamp, Leics LE8 0HG

ISBN: 978-0-7097-1879-6

Printed in China

LARGE PRINT

READY TO READ COLLECTION

Stories by Maureen Spurgeon
Illustrated by Gill Guile, Jenny Press, Stephen Holmes & Jane Swift

Brown Watson
ENGLAND

CONTENTS

WE LOVE HATTIE!

Hattie the Helicopter was landing at a big airport. 'Steady, Hattie,' said Roy, her pilot.

'We have fetched roses from Star Island!' Roy told a lady officer.

'Just in time for the visit by the Group Captain!' said the lady. 'Please stay and have a rest!'

'I never rest!' snorted a jumbo jet. 'And I fly around the world!'

'I have rescued people at sea,' said Hattie. 'And I have landed in the jungle!'

'Sssh!' came a voice. 'Here is the Group Captain!'

The Captain looked splendid in his uniform. 'Star Island roses!' he said. 'Look, Posy and Tim!'

'Oh, Grandpa,' said Tim. 'We wanted to go up in an aeroplane!'

'But these aircraft need a lot of fuel to make them go,' said the Captain. 'And they need lots of space to take off.' Then he saw Hattie. 'A helicopter!' he said. 'Now, that needs no space at all to take off. What about fuel, pilot?'

9

'Plenty in the tank, sir!' said Roy.

'Then let's go!' said the Captain. They got inside. Hattie's rotor blades whirred, taking them up into the sky.

'There is Star Island!' said the Captain. 'Steady, Hattie!'

Roy flew Hattie all around Star Island before landing back at the airport. 'That was great, Grandpa!' said Tim. 'Thank you!'

'You must thank Hattie!' said the Captain. 'She made it happen!'

'Yes!' said Posy. 'We LOVE Hattie the Helicopter!'

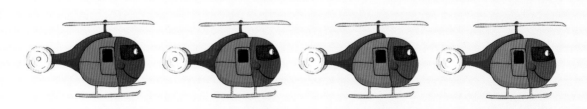

READ THESE WORDS AGAIN!

pilot	star
island	officer
visit	snorted
world	rescued
people	uniform
aeroplane	fuel
whirred	happen

12

WHAT CAN YOU SEE HERE?

Captain

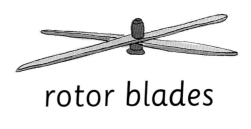

rotor blades

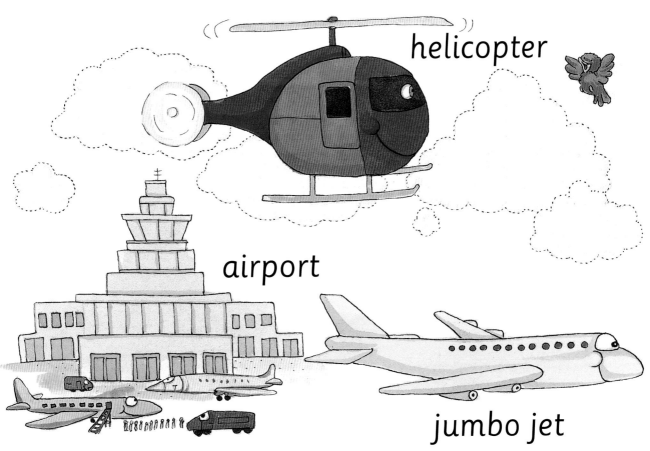

helicopter

airport

jumbo jet

THE KING AND THE WIZARD

'Oh, dear!' King Cole said to his servant, Sam. 'Wizard Woo teases the children. He makes cats bark and dogs quack! Now, he has just sent this message!'

Sam began to read aloud.

'I will come to the palace today to see King Cole. If he can tell me the first thing I am thinking, I shall go away for ever! If not, I shall be king!'

'If only Wizard Woo DID go away for good!' said the king.

Sam was looking at the king's crown and his red velvet robe.

'Oh, dear!' said King Cole. 'Do something, Sam!'

Sam called a footman. 'Bring Wizard Woo to me when he arrives!' he said.

'Sam!' said the king. 'How can you smile at a time like this?'

Wizard Woo also smiled when he arrived, seeing the crown and the red velvet gown.

'King Cole!' said Wizard Woo. 'Can you tell me the first thing I am thinking?'

'You think I am King Cole!' came the reply. 'That is the first thing you were thinking! True?'

'Yes,' said the wizard, 'but…'

Off came the crown and the robe. It was Sam! 'And you were thinking I was the king!' he said.

Wizard Woo flew into a rage!

'You have made me look a fool!' he cried. 'I am going!' And off he went.

'Peace at last!' said King Cole. 'My crown, please, Sam!'

'Of course!' smiled Sam.

READ THESE WORDS AGAIN!

king   teases
children   quack
message   aloud
come   palace
first   something
called   arrives
smile   smiled
reply   rage
peace   last

WHAT CAN YOU SEE HERE?

crown

wizard

footman

red velvet robe

servant

DON AND BIGGER DIGGER

Don the Digger had come to dig a sandpit at Barn School.

'Huh!' snorted Bigger Digger. 'A sandpit! I will be digging a road!'

'Our school is where Farmer Day's family home used to be,' Miss Foot was saying.

'And I do wish I was able to show you what it was like when I was a boy!' said Farmer Day.

Don went on digging. Then – CLANG!

'Hah!' said Bigger Digger. 'You are in trouble now!'

23

'Don hit an old, tin trunk,' said his driver. 'It was under the ground!'

'Grandad's trunk!' said Farmer Day. 'So that is where it was!'

Don scooped out the trunk. It was damp and rusty, but Farmer Day managed to lift the lid. So many things were inside!

'Grandma's milking stool!' cried Farmer Day. 'And the yoke she used to carry the pails of milk! Grandad's wind-up gramophone! And all these pictures!'

And that was not all.

There were toys and games, hoops and sticks, even some clothes!

'I want Barn School to have these things,' said Farmer Day. 'I wanted you to see how things used to be. Now I have my wish.'

'So, Don grants wishes!' said his driver. The children cheered.

'Don found the tin trunk!' said Miss Foot, happily.

'Don is a GREAT digger!' cried Farmer Day.

And Bigger Digger? He said nothing at all.

READ THESE WORDS AGAIN!

school	bigger
trouble	under
ground	scooped
pictures	hoops
sticks	clothes
wanted	grants
nothing	wishes

WHAT CAN YOU SEE HERE?

wind-up gramophone

yoke

digger

tin trunk

milking stool

TEDDY'S SPRING CLEAN

'The toy room needs a spring clean!' said Teddy. 'So much dust! Lots of tidying up to do!'

'Well, I'm not going to help!' said Stripey Tiger.

'And I'm not going to help!' said Mermaid Doll. 'What can we do?'

'I will put spots on your face and put my paw in a sling!' said Tiger. 'Teddy will think we are poorly!'

So Tiger painted red spots on Mermaid Doll. She put his paw in a sling. They did look poorly!

All this time, Mr. Potato had been helping Teddy Bear.

'You have worked hard, Mr. Potato!' said Teddy. 'You deserve a reward!' He went to the toy cupboard. 'Here you are!' he said. 'A bag of marbles and a puzzle!'

'Oh, thank you!' said Mr. Potato.

'Marbles and a puzzle!' said Mermaid Doll. 'Just for helping with the spring cleaning!'

Mermaid Doll rubbed the spots off her face. Stripey Tiger took his paw from out of the sling.

Mermaid Doll and Stripey Tiger both wanted to have something nice from Teddy's toy cupboard!

'Mermaid Doll and Tiger!' cried Teddy. 'What can I do for you?'

'Er, we came to help with the spring cleaning!' said Tiger.

'We want to tidy the toy cupboard!' said Mermaid Doll.

'That has been done already!' said Teddy. 'But, never mind! I am sure I can find LOTS more spring cleaning for you to do!' And, he did!

READ THESE WORDS AGAIN!

spring   clean
tidying   poorly
painted   helping
deserve   reward
marbles   puzzle
rubbed   both
wanted   something
already   sure

WHAT CAN YOU SEE HERE?

Stripey Tiger

Mr. Potato

Mermaid Doll

toy cupboard

paw in a sling

MINNIE AND MILLY

Ken drove Minnie the Minibus. They knew all the passengers, except one. She was an old lady who got on the bus each morning. She hardly spoke. She never smiled. Nobody even knew her name.

One day, as Minnie waited for the old lady, in jumped a little dog!

Tim Holt looked at the dog's collar.

'Look, John!' he said to his friend. 'Her name is Milly!'

'And there is an address,' said John. '10, Cherry Road.'

39

'I know where that is!' said Ken. 'Milly can come with us to town. Then we can take her back home.'

'Woof!' barked Milly. Everyone began to pat and stroke her, and all the time she was wagging her tail.

'All change!' cried Ken at the last stop. 'Time for a walk, Milly!'

Minnie felt sad when the time came to go back. It had been nice to have Milly on board and everyone talking about her.

'This is your stop, Milly!' said Ken. 'WOOF!' barked Milly.

'Milly!' cried a voice. 'Why did you run off?' It was the old lady.

'Woof!' barked Milly, her tail wagging again. 'Woof-woof!'

'She had your address on the disc on her collar,' explained Ken. 'Miss.. er'

'You can call me Dolly,' smiled the lady. 'I have not had Milly long. She is all I have to stop me from being lonely.'

'Well, now you know everyone on Minnie the Minibus,' said Ken. 'Thanks to Milly!'

'Woof!' barked Milly.

READ THESE WORDS AGAIN!

drove	except
morning	nobody
knew	jumped
friend	address
everyone	change
board	barked
lonely	know

WHAT CAN YOU SEE HERE?

passengers

disc

minibus

collar

old lady

I KNOW!

Tim was always saying, 'I know!'

'Tim,' said Luke, 'we are all going to the park...'

'I know!' said Tim. 'I know!'

'We are going to see a puppet show!' said Amita. 'And...'

'I know!' said Tim. 'I KNOW!'

'It is my birthday...' said Dan.

'I know!' said Tim. 'I KNOW!'

Then, Tim went off to the park! But there was nobody there.

Tim gave a shout. 'Hey!'

'Hey!' a voice came from the Wendy house. It was the echo of his own voice, but Tim did not know that! 'Where is the puppet show?' he shouted.

'Puppet show!' came the echo.

'I know!' shouted Tim. 'It is over here!'

'Over here!' came the echo.

Tim searched the Wendy house. It was empty. 'Hey!' he cried. 'I want the puppet show!'

'Puppet show!' came the echo yet again. 'Puppet show!'

49

Tim marched off in a temper.

'Where is Tim?' he heard someone saying. 'He said he knew about the puppet show for my birthday!'

Tim looked over a fence. Everyone was in Dan's garden, enjoying the puppet show!

'Hello, Tim!' said Dan. 'You are a bit late for my party!'

'But you can come to the park for some games!' said Luke.

'Pity you missed the puppet show, Tim!' said Amita.

'Yes,' said Tim. 'I know.'

READ THESE WORDS AGAIN!

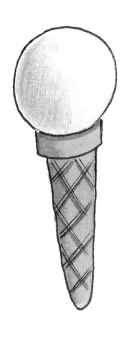

always	saying
know	birthday
there	nobody
voice	echo
shouted	here
searched	empty
marched	temper
knew	everyone
enjoying	missed

WHAT CAN YOU SEE HERE?

swing

puppet show

Wendy house

fence

garden

AMY THE AMBULANCE

'Calling Amy the Ambulance! Susan Mills has had a fall in Hill Park. Bring her to hospital! Over!'

Jo, Amy's driver, flicked a switch on her radio. 'Amy calling! We are on our way! Over and out!'

Susan was crying. 'My arm hurts! And my doll is broken!'

'It is her arm that is broken!' said Nurse Paula. 'Amy the Ambulance will take you both to hospital!'

'I do not want to go to hospital!' sobbed Susan.

'Dina cannot go alone,' said Mum.

Susan gave a sniff. She stopped crying. 'All right,' she said.

Paula helped Susan into Amy the Ambulance. 'Dina needs a plaster on her face,' she said. 'Let us find one in Amy's first-aid box!' Susan put a plaster on Dina's face. Then she helped to bandage Dina's leg.

At the hospital, a doctor took an X-ray picture of Susan's arm. 'You have broken your arm,' he said. 'We must put it in a plaster cast. It will mend in six weeks.'

Later, Paula put Dina's broken arm in plaster, too. 'Dina's plaster cannot come off,' said Mum. 'Toys cannot mend like we can, Susan.'

Susan stroked Dina's hair. 'I do not think she minds,' she said, 'as long as she can stay with Amy!'

'Good idea!' said Paula. 'With her big smile, her arm in a sling and a plaster on her face, she will make everyone feel better about going to hospital!'

'Yes!' said Susan. 'And Amy the Ambulance will be taking them!'

READ THESE WORDS AGAIN!

driver	flicked
switch	radio
crying	broken
nurse	hospital
sobbed	plaster
bandage	cannot
stroked	everyone

WHAT CAN YOU SEE HERE?

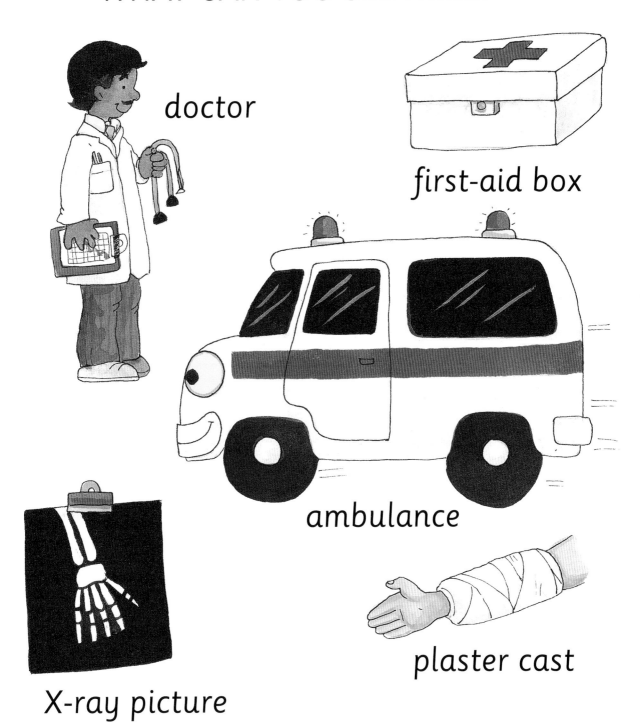

doctor

first-aid box

ambulance

X-ray picture

plaster cast

BELLA'S UMBRELLA

Bella Bear had a new umbrella.

'Just see my new umbrella!' Bella kept saying. 'I can hardly wait for a rainy day, so that I can use it!'

She looked up at the sky, watching out for any sign of rain, just one, little black cloud! But the sky was a clear blue, without a cloud to be seen. She waited for the first shower of raindrops. But the sun shone high in the sky.

But Bella wanted to show off her new umbrella!

'I will go to the park!' she said at last. 'The ducks will be splashing about in the pond. I can pretend to get wet and put up my umbrella!'

It seemed hotter than ever in the park! Even the ducks were hiding among the water weeds.

'No sign of rain!' said Bella with a sigh. 'And I DID want to put up my pretty new umbrella!'

She walked on, getting hotter and hotter. Then – splash! Water splashed on her head. Then, again. Splash! Was it raining?

Bella put up her pretty new umbrella. Then she looked round. It was a splash from the water fountain! She felt very silly.

'Bella!' cried Pretty Bear. 'What a pretty parasol! A parasol to shade you from the sun!'

'A – a parasol?' said Bella. She looked up at her umbrella.

'Yes!' said Pretty. 'I must get one!'

'So, when it is fine, my umbrella is a parasol,' said Bella. 'And when it rains, my parasol is an umbrella!'

READ THESE WORDS AGAIN!

pretty	wait
looked	sky
sign	clear
shone	high
park	ducks
pretend	hiding
sigh	hotter
splash	fountain

WHAT CAN YOU SEE HERE?

black cloud

umbrella

shower of raindrops

water weeds

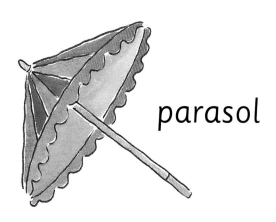

parasol

HERE COMES JESSIE!

All the animals at the big safari park knew Jessie the Jeep! She was always busy, bringing things for them or taking Wendy, her driver, around the safari park.

One day, Wendy drove the vet to see a monkey and her baby.

'The baby is still small,' said the vet 'But she is doing well!'

'Good!' said the keeper. 'It is the first baby for that monkey!'

'Come on, Jessie!' smiled Wendy. 'You can see Baby Monkey later!'

Jessie fetched hay and blankets for the donkeys. She worked hard all day. Then Wendy got a call on her radio.

'Baby Monkey is missing!' cried the keeper. 'Have you seen her?'

'No!' said Wendy. 'I shall drive around the safari park in Jessie!'

'Good idea!' said the keeper. 'The monkey is fretting badly! And the baby needs her mother!'

They looked all over the safari park.

'It will be dark soon!' said Wendy. 'We must find her!'

'We are all worried!' said the keeper. 'Only Jessie doesn't seem upset!'

'I feel cold!' said Wendy. 'I left my jacket on the back seat!'

She reached across – and touched something furry! It was Baby Monkey, fast asleep!

'Well!' said Wendy. 'Thanks, Jessie!'

Baby Monkey liked riding in Jessie! And when she saw her baby, Mother Monkey jumped up on the jeep!

'Look at that!' said Wendy. 'ALL the animals DO know Jessie the Jeep!'

READ THESE WORDS AGAIN!

knew	animals
busy	driver
around	baby
small	later
fetched	blankets
idea	worried
jacket	know

WHAT CAN YOU SEE HERE?

jeep

vet

safari park

monkeys

donkeys

DOZY DORMOUSE!

Dozy Dormouse was fast asleep.

'Dozy Dormouse,' said Squirrel, 'is asleep AGAIN!'

'Quack!' went Duck. 'Sleep is no use at all!'

'So much to do, instead of sleeping!' said Rabbit.

Dozy slept until the next day. Then, as soon as he woke up, he began running about, picking up ears of corn and nuts and berries! Next, he dug a hole, deep in the ground!

'Dozy IS busy!' said Rabbit.

'Now, he is eating without stopping!' said Squirrel. 'He is hungry after all that work!'

Then, after Dozy had eaten all the food, he crawled into his hole and curled up into a ball.

'Well!' sniffed Rabbit. 'Dozy is going to sleep again!'

'Sleep is no use!' said Squirrel.

'You do not think so?' came the deep voice of Stag. 'See the falling leaves! Feel the cold wind! Winter is coming!'

'Winter!' quacked Duck. 'My pond will be frozen!'

'We will need to search for food!' said Squirrel.

'And try to keep warm!' said Rabbit with a shiver.

'But Dozy will sleep the winter away, until the warm weather comes,' said Stag.

They looked into the hole, where Dozy was already fast asleep.

'So, sleep is useful after all,' said Rabbit. 'See you in the spring, Dozy Dormouse!'

READ THESE WORDS AGAIN!

fast   asleep
duck   quack
instead   picking
about   ground
hungry   work
crawled   curled
sniffed   leaves
frozen   already

WHAT CAN YOU SEE HERE?

 squirrel

berries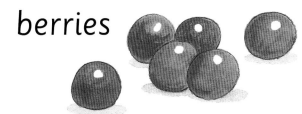

 Dozy Dormouse

 rabbit

 stag

MITCH, THE MAILVAN

Mitch the Mailvan had almost finished work. When the day began, he had been loaded up with letters, cards, parcels and packets. Now, there was one parcel left.

'Who is this for, Mitch?' asked Dave. 'The label is torn. I can only read Mi... I know! It must be for Miss Dixon, the baker!'

But the parcel was not for Miss Dixon. 'So, who is it for?' said Dave. 'I can only read Mi...'

'I think I know!' said Miss Dixon.

And off she went without another word.

'Mi..' read Dave again. 'Who is this for, Mitch? I know! It must be Mike Bond at the garage!'

But the parcel was not for Mike.

'So, who is it for?' said Dave. 'Look! I can just make out Mi…'

'I think I know!' said Mike. And off he went without another word.

'Mi..' said Dave, trying to read the label again. 'Who is this for, Mitch? I know! It must be Mill Lane School!'

But the parcel was not for Mill Lane School.

'So, who is it for?' said Dave.

Then, Mitch saw Miss Dixon and Mike Bond, together with all the children at Mill Lane School.

'Open it!' they shouted all together. 'Open the parcel!'

So, Dave opened the parcel. And inside was a shiny new name-plate with the name 'MITCH' on it.

'Well, well!' smiled Dave. 'Now, we know who the parcel was for!'

READ THESE WORDS AGAIN!

almost   finished

loaded   letters

cards   packets

who   only

think   know

another   word

garage   school

together   open

WHAT CAN YOU SEE HERE?

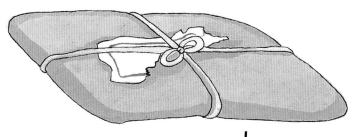

parcel

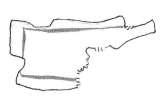

label

mailvan

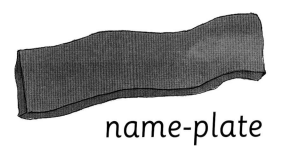

name-plate

children

93

THE BARBECUE DRAGON

When Dilly the Dragon roared, flames came out of his mouth.

Then, it started to rain and Dilly got cold. There was no roar. No flames.

'My fire is out!' he said. 'I must breathe air to make flames. There is plenty of fresh air in the forest!'

In the forest there was a notice – BEWARE OF FIRE. 'Very wise,' said Dilly. 'But I need MY fire!' Another notice said – FIRE CAUSES DAMAGE. 'True,' said Dilly. 'But I NEED my fire!'

95

Another notice said – PUT FIRES OUT! Poor Dilly felt so cold!

'No fires, today!' a voice was saying. 'It is too cold and damp!'

'So, can we have our barbecue party, Linda?' a girl called out.

'I do not think so, Penny,' said Linda. 'It is raining again! Quick! We must shelter in the forest!'

Dilly went over to the barbecue. It was still warm. He breathed in, feeling warmer inside. Just as the rain stopped – R-OA-OA-RR! – flames came out of his mouth!

'What was that?' a boy called out. 'It sounded like thunder!' Everyone went to see.

'There is a fire for our barbecue!' cried Penny. 'We can have our party!'

'That dragon helped us!' said Holly. 'He roared like thunder and breathed flames! I saw him!'

'Dragons?' said Linda. 'Dragons are only for story books, Holly!'

'But I DID see him!' said Holly with a smile. 'Really, I did!' And just then, Dilly let out another roar.

R-OA-OA-RR!

READ THESE WORDS AGAIN!

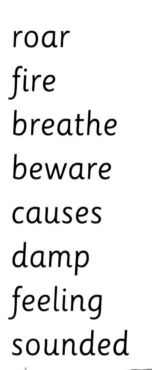

roar

fire

breathe

beware

causes

damp

feeling

sounded

flames

mouth

plenty

another

damage

shelter

warmer

thunder

WHAT CAN YOU SEE HERE?

dragon

forest

barbecue

BEWARE OF FIRE

notice

story books

TUBBY AND SPEEDY

Tubby the Tractor did not go very fast. Speedy the Sports Car was always teasing him.

'Hoot! Hoot!' he hooted, speeding down the lane. 'See how I race along!'

'Stop!' cried Farmer Bell. 'You have made my chickens run off!'

'You have scared the sheep!' said Tubby. But Speedy did not care.

It began to rain. For the rest of the day and all night, it rained hard. Next day Tubby had to go even slower across the muddy ground.

'Poor old Tubby!' hooted Speedy. 'I can go fast, rain or no rain!' SPLASH! Speedy went right into a big puddle, drenching the sheep in muddy water! 'Hoot! Hoot!' hooted Speedy. 'Hoot! Hoot!'

The rain had made the lane very wet and VERY slippery. Speedy was going much too fast...

'HOOT!' Now, Speedy was slipping and skidding. He tried to slow down. He tried to stop.

'Look out!' shouted Farmer Bell. 'The pond!' But it was too late.

SPLASH! Now, Speedy was drenched in water!

'Come on, Tubby,' said Farmer Bell. He drove him to the edge of the pond. Then he tied one end of a rope to Tubby's tow bar and the other end to Speedy's bumper.

'Now!' said Farmer Bell. 'Pull!' Tubby did enjoy pulling Speedy out of the pond! Towing him back down the lane was even more fun!

'Hoot! Hoot!' went Tubby the Tractor. 'Now I am going MUCH faster than you, Speedy!'

READ THESE WORDS AGAIN!

teasing   hooted
speeding   chickens
scared   sheep
rained   slower
muddy   ground
splash   puddle
drenching   slippery
tried   enjoy

WHAT CAN YOU SEE HERE?

tractor

farmer

sports car

tow bar

pond

WHERE IS TINY?

Princess Fay loved her cat, Tiny. Tiny had been a present on her last birthday. 'So, what do you want this year?' asked the queen.

'I want to have Tiny with me all the time,' said Princess Fay.

'That is not easy,' said the queen. 'We must see what we can do!'

Next day, the princess called her cat. 'Tiny! Tiny, where are you?'

But Tiny did not appear until tea-time. She looked very pleased with herself.

'Tiny!' cried Princess Fay. 'Oh, Tiny, do not run off again!'

But Tiny was away for most of the next day and the day after. Princess Fay was nearly in tears. 'Oh, Tiny!' she cried. 'Where have you been?' But Tiny just looked pleased with herself.

Next day, Princess Fay got up early. 'My birthday!' she cried. 'Now, where is Tiny? Tiny!'

Then, as Princess Fay started searching, she saw the queen in the rose garden.

She was sitting at an easel with her painting things. And there beside her was Tiny! 'I have finished my painting!' smiled the queen. 'Come and see!'

Princess Fay looked. It was a painting of Tiny!

'I shall put the painting in a frame,' said the queen. 'So you CAN have Tiny with you all the time, just as you wanted. Happy birthday, Fay!'

Princess Fay was so happy, she had nothing to say. And, Tiny? She looked pleased with herself!

READ THESE WORDS AGAIN!

loved	present
birthday	what
called	appear
looked	pleased
herself	next
where	nearly
tears	searching
sitting	there
wanted	happy

WHAT CAN YOU SEE HERE?

princess

rose garden

queen

easel

painting in a frame

TAMMY'S SURPRISE FARE

'Taxi!' Tammy the Taxi was always busy!

'I hope we do not have to go far,' said Ted, her driver. 'I want to see a football match on television!'

'Taxi!' a man cried. 'Will you take me to the railway station?'

'Certainly!' said Ted. They soon got there. Then, as the man paid his fare, there came the cry, 'Taxi!'

It was a lady with lots of luggage.

'Can you take me to the airport?' she asked.

'Certainly,' said Ted. The airport was further away. When they got there, someone else cried, 'Taxi!'

'Please take us to the Town Hotel!' It was a man with his wife and children.

'Certainly!' said Ted. They had hardly reached the hotel when someone else cried 'Taxi!'

'A waitress has had a fall!' said a porter. 'Please, take her to hospital!'

The hospital was even further away. But Tammy hoped Ted might get home in time to see the football match.

121

'Taxi!' This time, it was the Mayor. 'I have been visiting the hospital and it is nearly time for my next appointment. Can I go in your taxi?'

'Certainly,' said Ted, further from home than ever. 'Where to, sir?'

'North End football stadium!' said the mayor. 'There is a match tonight! Why not come and see the game with me? That is, if you are not doing anything else!'

'Thanks,' grinned Ted. 'Tammy the Taxi and I, we were only going home to watch television!'

READ THESE WORDS AGAIN!

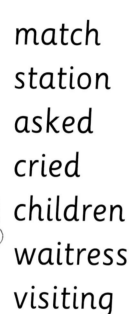

match	railway
station	fare
asked	further
cried	hotel
children	porter
waitress	hoped
visiting	appointment

WHAT CAN YOU SEE HERE?

television

luggage

taxi

mayor

football stadium

BUZZ, BUZZ, BUSY BEES!

'Silly bees!' said Farmer. 'There is no pollen inside the flowers on these tiles on my kitchen wall!' He opened a window. 'Buzz off! Find real flowers!'

'Buzz! Buzz-z-z!' went the bees.

'These bees!' said Hector Horse. 'As they buzz around collecting pollen to make honey, they help plants to make new plants. They want pollen from the flowers on your hat, Donny Donkey!'

'But my flowers are plastic!' said Donny. 'Buzz off, bees!'

Clara Cow was eating grass in the meadow. 'These bees!' she mooed. 'They are all buzzing around these lovely buttercups!'

'They want pollen so that they can make honey!' said Hector.

'And as bees collect pollen, they help plants to make new plants,' said Donny. 'Look! They are going to the vegetable patch! Which flowers will they find there?'

'Let us go and see!' said Hector.

Peas, tomatoes and cabbages all grew in the vegetable patch.

The bees did not bother with those!
They buzzed busily around the orange
flowers of the runner beans and the
yellow flowers of the marrows!
'Buzz-buzzzz!'

'See these bees!' said Donny. 'They
are collecting pollen to make honey for
the farmer!'

'And they are helping plants to make
new plants,' said Hector again. 'That
means new crops of winter feed for us!'

'What busy bees!' mooed Clara.

'Buzz-buzz-z-z!' went the bees.

READ THESE WORDS AGAIN!

silly	flowers
tiles	buzz
collecting	cabbages
plastic	grass
meadow	new
honey	peas
tomatoes	buttercups
orange	yellow
marrows	busy

WHAT CAN YOU SEE HERE?

bees

pollen

vegetable patch

runner beans

marrows

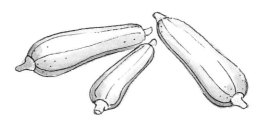

IDA IS ON HER WAY!

Ding-dong! Ding-dong! Everyone liked seeing Ida the Ice-Cream Van on a hot summer's day. Ice-cream cones, milkshakes, choc ices... her customers liked them all.

'It has been a busy summer,' said Rob as he drove Ida home.

'Yes,' agreed his girlfriend, Rosie. 'But Ida will not have many customers when winter comes.'

What Rosie said was true. On cold days, nobody came to buy ice creams, milkshakes or choc ices.

One day, Rob pushed Ida out into the road. 'Cleaning time, Ida!' he said. 'Then we'll cover you up so you can keep warm all winter.'

'I do not want that!' Ida said to herself. 'I want to be out on the road, seeing all my customers!'

Then, just as Rob was polishing Ida's headlamps, along came a lorry.

'Hi!' called the driver. 'Any idea where I can get something to eat for myself and my mate?'

'No,' said Rosie. 'But I can put some tea into a flask for you.'

'And I can heat up some sausage rolls!' said Rob.

'Thanks!' said the driver. 'We have been looking for somewhere to eat for hours! Seeing your smart van made us stop and ask!'

So, Rosie went to make the tea and Rob went to heat up some sausage rolls to put in a bag. And they both had the same idea...

Ding-dong! Ding-dong! Now, everyone likes seeing Ida on a winter's day! Hot drinks, pies, rolls, burgers...customers like them all!

READ THESE WORDS AGAIN!

everyone	summer
girlfriend	cleaning
cover	winter
polishing	herself
called	idea
something	myself
mate	somewhere
burgers	ask

WHAT CAN YOU SEE HERE?

milkshake

customers

ice-cream van

flask

sausage roll

HELLO, HOBBY-HORSE!

Hobby-Horse stood in the broom cupboard. He was a fine hobby-horse with knots all along his mane, reins and a harness with yellow bells. But, he was lonely.

'Nobody even knows I am here anymore,' he told himself.

But, one day, the door was pulled open. 'Hey! Nita!' said a voice he had never heard before. 'A Hobby-Horse! He must have been here before we came! You can ride him in the town parade on Sunday!'

143

'He is not a real horse, Max,' came a second voice. 'You know that...'

'But you can go where you like on Hobby-Horse!' said Max. 'He will be better than a real horse!'

Hobby-Horse did not know about that. 'A real horse can trot and gallop,' he said to himself. 'I can only move with someone pushing me along on my wheels.'

But on Sunday, Nita took him into the street. Then she sat across his back, pushing him along with her feet, so that his wheels went round.

'Money for the animal shelter, please!' she cried, holding out a bucket. In and out among the crowds they went, with everyone wanting to give money and to get to know Hobby-Horse!

'And I can get around on MY hobby-horse!' cried Max. 'Look!' Nita looked. And Hobby-Horse looked. Max was on a hobby-horse with black knots along his mane!

'Another hobby-horse!' said Hobby-Horse. 'I will never be lonely again!' And he never was.

READ THESE WORDS AGAIN!

knots	yellow
lonely	nobody
himself	pulled
voice	heard
parade	Sunday
second	know
gallop	pushing
wheels	another

WHAT CAN YOU SEE HERE?

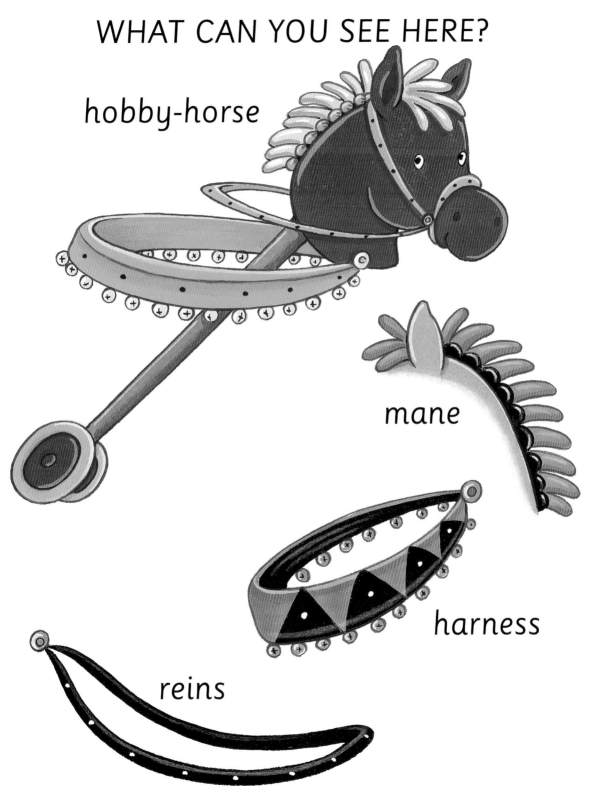

hobby-horse

mane

harness

reins

NO LEAVES ON THE LINE!

Eddie liked being a steam engine, even though he only pulled trucks on a goods line. Dennis the Diesel pulled the trains on the main line.

'How slow you are!' he snorted at Eddie. 'Still, you only pull trucks!'

'I am as good as you are!' Eddie puffed. But Dennis whizzed past.

The days began to get shorter. The leaves were beginning to fall.

'More coal in your fire-box, Eddie!' said Dave, his driver. 'We need lots of steam today!'

153

'Coal!' cried Dennis. 'Steam! Hah!'

Eddie was just getting up steam, when there was a loud screech.

'Sounds like Dennis is in trouble on the main line!' said Dave. 'And just listen to those passengers!'

The passengers were very cross!

'Why has the train stopped?'

'What is wrong with the engine?'

'Fallen leaves are clogging up the line!' said the driver. 'The engine cannot move!'

A man pointed at Eddie. 'That engine is moving!' he said.

'The sparks from Eddie's fire-box burn up leaves as soon as they fall!' said Dave. 'Leaves on the line are no problem for us!'

'Then Eddie can pull our train!' said an important-looking man. 'I am a director of the railway!'

So Dennis was shunted away and Eddie puffed down the line, burning all the leaves as he went.

'Hurrah!' cried the passengers.

'Hurrah!' puffed Eddie.

And if Dennis did say anything, nobody heard him.

155

READ THESE WORDS AGAIN!

leaves	pulled
trains	main
snorted	whizzed
shorter	screech
trouble	wrong
clogging	heard
important	director
burning	move

WHAT CAN YOU SEE HERE?

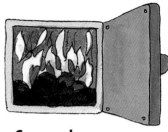

fire-box

diesel engine

passengers

steam engine

driver

FAIRY PANSY

'How can I see a human child?' Fairy Pansy asked Fairy Moth.

'There is one at the end of our garden!' said Fairy Moth. 'Such lovely hair, tiny feet, a sweet face and a soft voice! Wait and see!'

So Fairy Pansy hid among the flowers, waiting. After a while, there came the sound of footsteps. Fairy Pansy peeped out – only to see big, flat feet with heavy boots. And the face did not look sweet at all!

'Fairies at the bottom of our garden, Meg?' came a voice. 'Huh!'

Fairy Pansy peeped out again. She still hoped to see a sweet face with long hair. But the face was round, with a snub nose and short hair.

'Mark!' came another voice. 'What are you staring at?'

'Er…' came the reply. 'For a moment, I was sure I saw…er…'

'Fairies at the bottom of our garden?' finished Meg. 'That is what I am always saying, Mark!'

Mark walked off, kicking at the grass. But Meg parted some of the flowers and looked more closely. Fairy Pansy sat among the flowers, her face in her tiny hands.

'Well!' breathed Meg. 'I SAID there were fairies at the bottom of our garden!'

Fairy Pansy took her hands away. She saw the lovely face, the long hair and the smooth skin.

'At last!' she said in her soft, tiny voice. 'I have seen a REAL human child!'

READ THESE WORDS AGAIN!

fairy	asked
tiny	soft
voice	waiting
sound	footsteps
peeped	only
smooth	bottom
hoped	round
moment	breathed
staring	reply

WHAT CAN YOU SEE HERE?

 fairies

garden

a human child

a snub nose

heavy boots

FIRE ENGINE FRED

Fire Engine Fred was at the Town Show. 'Can I work the hose?' asked a boy.

'There is no fire!' said Fireman Tim. 'You can sound the bell instead!'

CLANG-CLANG! The boy enjoyed ringing Fred's bell! But Fred DID wish that there WAS a fire to put out!

All the way back to the fire station, Fred kept thinking about putting out a real fire. Then he saw a tall swirl of black smoke...

167

'Fire!' shouted Fireman Bill, clanging the bell. 'There is a fire at Betty Baker's cottage!'

Fred raced to the cottage.

'Get the hose, Bill!' said Tim. 'Fix it to the water-tap and aim it at the window! I am going inside!'

There was smoke inside the cottage!

'Betty!' cried Tim. 'Let me carry you into the garden, away from the fire!'

'There is NO fire!' cried Betty. 'I burnt some bread, so I opened the window to let the smoke out!'

Poor Tim! 'We have soaked your kitchen with water from Fred's hose!' he said. 'I am so sorry.'

Betty smiled. 'Fred is enjoying the sunshine!' she said. 'Bring my things out here to dry and then we can do the same! We can all have some of the cakes I have baked!'

'We are glad you did not have a real fire!' said Bill.

'So am I!' said Betty. 'And it is good to know that you and Fire Engine Fred are always ready to help when people need you!'

READ THESE WORDS AGAIN!

asked	sound
instead	clang
enjoyed	swirl
smoke	cottage
raced	cakes
opened	kitchen
sorry	people

WHAT CAN YOU SEE HERE?

hose

fire station

fireman

long ladder

fire engine

MOLE FINDS A HOME

Mole lived in a long, dark, damp tunnel. He did not like his home!

'This is where we are safe,' said Father Mole. 'It is fine for us!'

'It is not fine for ME!' said Mole to himself. 'I am leaving!'

He went along the tunnel. Just ahead was a hole. Sunshine beamed down. Mole climbed and poked his head outside. Just as he did, a spade appeared above him and almost hit him on the head! The man digging the hole hadn't even noticed Mole!

Mole ran under a hedge, as quickly as he could. Then, something round and hard landed on the ground next to him.

'What a hit!' came a voice. 'Where did that cricket ball go?'

Mole ran off and escaped down a rabbit hole. He bumped right into a big rabbit!

'Out of our home,' cried the rabbit, 'You are frightening my babies!'

Poor Mole! Suddenly, he felt very lonely and tired. Then he heard a voice he knew.

'So there you are, Mole! Where did you go?' It was Father Mole!

'I found a lawn,' panted Mole. 'But a man didn't notice me and almost hit me on the head with a spade! Then a cricket ball just missed me, so I ran down a hole and a rabbit shouted at me!'

'And now you are just in time for dinner!' said Mother Mole.

Mole opened his mouth to speak again. Then he looked around the tunnel, sniffing its smells and feeling the soft ground. It was so good to be home!

READ THESE WORDS AGAIN!

dark	damp
tunnel	where
leaving	sunshine
beamed	climbed
appeared	digging
another	cricket
escaped	suddenly
man	there
missed	sniffing

WHAT CAN YOU SEE HERE?

mole

lawn

spade

hedge

baby rabbits

CLARA, AT HOME AND AWAY

To Todd and Una, Clara the Caravan was a friend. With Clara being towed by the family car, they went to stay at the seaside, in camping parks, forests and woods.

'I like going to bed in Clara's pull-down bunks!' said Todd.

'I like keeping all our toys in Clara's lockers,' said Una.

'But it will soon be time for us to go back to school,' said Todd.

'We will miss being in Clara,' said Una. They felt sad about that.

'Cheer up!' said Mum. 'Clara will be taking us to Uncle Tony's wedding this weekend!'

Uncle Tony lived in an apartment block. In the grounds was a big garden. And in the garden was a marquee, like a big tent.

'This is for our wedding party!' said Uncle Tony. 'You can put Clara here!'

It was a nice wedding. But being with Clara made it even nicer.

'I DO like your caravan!' said Sally, Uncle Tony's wife. 'It must be such fun, staying inside!'

'Come and see us!' said Mum. 'Then you can stay in Clara, too!'

'Can we stay in Clara?' asked Una. 'When we go home, I mean?'

'That is a good idea!' said Mum.

So when she is not taking them on trips to the seaside, forests or camping parks, Clara is a playroom for Una and Todd, where they can invite friends. And there is always room for visitors!

'Being with Clara is as much fun at home as when we go away!' said Todd. 'She is a real friend!'

187

READ THESE WORDS AGAIN!

friend	towed
family	lockers
school	uncle
grounds	wedding
party	nicer
inside	idea
invite	visitors

WHAT CAN YOU SEE HERE?

caravan

pull-down bunks

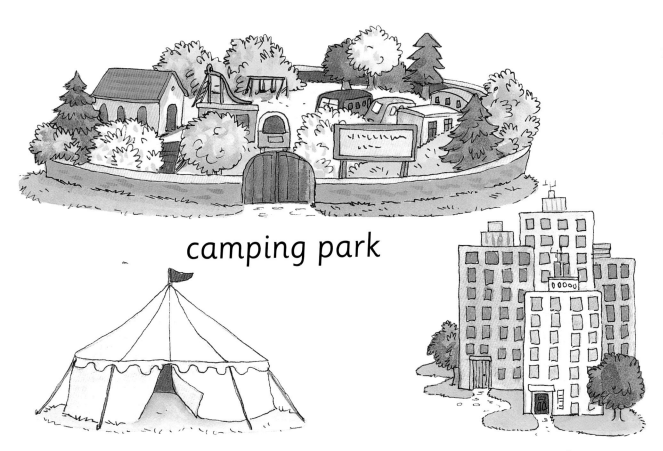

camping park

marquee

apartment block